PILGRIMAGE

© 1996 Ian Slater

ISBN 1 85072 191 2

Printed in Plantin typeface
by Sessions of York
The Ebor Press
York, England

Pilgrimage

Ian Slater

*This book is addressed to that of God,
and to that of the child, in everyone*

William Sessions Limited
York, England

Pilgrimage

Where is my home? Where has the river fled
That nightly soothed me with the distant sound
Of deep, dark waters rolling? Where the bed
On which I slept? – And where the native ground
That nourished me from childhood, through the ways
Of discontented youth, then let me grow
To manhood? Where the sweetness of the days
Of tireless Beauty? – Where did Beauty go?
The evening falls; a drowsy weariness
Wraps up the world in shadows, and I see
But faintly now the springtime's wild excess
That thrilled the morning with its brilliancy:
Spectral, the vision rises in my mind
Trailing the glory years I left behind.

Morning

IT WAS A LONG NIGHT to the awakening, but when the early rays of the sun and the lowing of the cows roused me from my sleep it seemed as though there had never been night at all. Strange and wonderful were the dreams which had haunted me while I slept, but when I awoke I was able to recall their marvels and mysteries only in pale phantoms of thought which day doomed swiftly from my mind.

But now the cock has crowed, and it is morning in my world; the sun is already high, sheep straggle and graze on the hillsides, the fresh-milked cows go out into the fields, and the fervour of life has begun.

After my first long-lingering, loving adoration of the hills, I dress and walk down the stairs to the kitchen where a full breakfast replete with homely dishes awaits me on the table; but I do not do justice to the meal and eat it quickly, ravenous for my first taste of the morning's breath, on my first morning home.

As I leave the house I am dressed to meet all the various moods of the weather which May can deal in my native region, and I fill my lungs to the limits, breathing deep, deeper, deeply to the point of dizziness, the pure country air that wafts from the forest, over the hills, and through the dewy fields to greet me in the garden.

Cleansed on the night and fresh as the morning, my senses are sharpened and flood my brain until it is teeming with sensation; in such a state of heightened perception one could soon become inebriate, and indeed it is a little while before I am again able to become aware of the pulse of my thoughts.

But what are my thoughts, now that I have reached my journey's end and no longer need memory's pilgrim-staff to aid me through the world? My thoughts are incoherent, they are fugues of ideas and impressions with neither form nor shape; only a joyous leit-motiv which runs throughout has any semblence of continuity as it sings again and again, 'I am home, I am home'.

It is an old song and one I have often sung, but now the words are altered; I have sung it in foreign lands and in the hearts of cities, at sea and in the mountains, wherever I have loved its music has played, and wherever I have been lonely it has brought comfort to me. It is a song which is older than myself, when I was born it was already old, and when I am dead it will live on, for it is the song of eternity; but now; for a short while, it mingles its life with mine.

I have no plans for journeying today for I have achieved the goal of my pilgrimage and thus can rest in peace; to love shall be my only desire, and to sing shall be my only song.

Calm cradling hills mild-mother me; the sun
My fearless father shines; my sisters bleed
Beauty among milch-meadowlands; I run
Brothered by rivers, breathless as they speed
My journey down the dalliance of day
To where the greenworld in a golden glow
Gathers its greatness gloriously, and May
Familial fires the magic of the flow.

The Town

IT IS RAINING, and it seems fitting that this should be the case as I walk the narrow cobbled streets, for it is the usual weather of the town.

As the rain washes away the dust of yesterday, so should I wash away old memories from my mind and view the town as it really is, not through eyes half-misted by nostalgia, but through eyes which see clearly and dwell not only on the past but also on the present. But it is impossible; unlike dust mental images of the past cannot be washed away, and perversely I am thankful that they superimpose themselves on present reality.

Sometimes though, there is a mingling of past and present, and the streets whose appearance memory has held in ageless encapsulation are unchanged even to the very people who inhabit them; perhaps these people are older, but they are yet recognisably those amongst whom I moved in the dallying days of youth.

Neither has the language of the town changed. It is still as defiantly regional as if it had never encountered the influence of radio, television and cinema, and the bland colourless tones of 'accepted' speech. Still sounds the unaltered accent; the old, and often nonsensical phrases and expressions; the idiosyncracies of a grammar unknown to the rest of the country. There is something comforting about this rough unpolished speech, and again and again I catch myself smiling as another familiar phrase falls on my ears. My smile is not that of an amused visitor to whom such utterances would seem outlandish in the extreme, but the smile of one to whom such language evokes the essence of his formative years; the smile of contentment at knowing that all is right with the world – for this is the language of innocence.

Yes, I am happy here, as happy as it is possible to be; my heart is full of affection, and were I of a more demonstrative nature I would no doubt kiss the ground on which I walk.

Even today, I feel that same passionate love for the town I had felt when I was one of its inhabitants, in the days when I had the ability to look at the town as though it were not only the scene in which I existed, but also the stage on which I would act out my life.

But since those early days I have played the role of spectator far much more than I have that of participant, although whether this has been wise I am unable to say. Wise is it only to be wise. Certainly by spectating one is able to perceive and understand intricacies which the participant can only experience with all his senses occupied by the task in hand. Alas, though, for the spectator, for him the loneliness of the world is ever at hand, and love and admire as he will, his love and admiration are neither shared nor answered even though it may well be that he is the greatest lover in the world. This being the case, I loved the town intensely, whilst – after I had been given the power of thought – neither believing nor feeling that I was part of its daily life.

But today no thoughts of discontent shall disturb me, and for a while I will throw off my spectator's garb and don that of the participant; I shall walk the streets unnoticing which houses still stand and which have been demolished, I shall not listen wonderingly at the dear familiar speech, I shall disregard the feel of the cobbles beneath my feet, I shall smell no breath of moorland air as it sweeps down from the hillsides, neither shall I taste the bitterness nor the sweetness of remembering; today I shall simply be.

Mild in the middle morning of my tears
And carefree over clouds beneath my youth,
Buoyant beyond the breeze I wore my years
As springtime bore the soaring of its truth;
And glorious on the great wings of my race,
I rode the furious freedom of my force,
And ravaged rainbows in their resting place,
And – conquering – crowned creation in my course;
Only the distant greenhill harbouring high
My unmapped heaven motioned me to make
A space for graceless haste to hurry by –
I kept my quiet there. – Wide in the wake
Of my mad-meteor-rioting rampage,
I cousined calm, and hallowed heritage.

The School

IT IS ALL so much smaller than I remembered, that I find it hard to believe that in this small building and this small yard I shared six years of my childhood with 200 others of my generation. And yet in reality so little has changed in the aspect of the building and so little has altered in the prospect of the yard, that I am able to acknowledge them instantaneously as the school and playground of my early years.

Today the classrooms are empty and the playground is quiet; of all their former inhabitants only I am here.

The playground gate has been left open and I have walked in where formerly I ran. How strange it all seems, I feel as though I have no right to be here, for was not every lesson that I learned in this school taught to me with the sole purpose of guiding me away from it and into the world? The feeling of strangeness does not pass even though, in rapid succession, I see countless features of my surroundings which awake long-forgotten winters, springs and summers in my autumnal mind.

Here I played marbles, it was always summer then; against this wall I broke my nose sliding on snow and ice on a robust winter day; everywhere there was skipping and singing, hopscotch and rounders, laughing and crying, football and fighting, shouting and speaking, cartwheels and handstands, P.T. and standing in lines, the blowing of the whistles and the clang of the brass school-bell.

I pace the playground restlessly, remembering: the head-mistress, crabbed and strict and feared by all; the music teacher, huge as a jelly in a black silk dress; the ever hated maths lessons; smells of rubber and chalk; flowers in jam-jars, tadpoles and stickle-backs; stars for doing well; the pliability of Plasticene; ink wells, ink powder, crayons and pencils, plaits and pens and paint. I remember my first day, but not in every detail – only with whom I sat, and that the first things we learned were how to flick tiny square cardboard letters of the alphabet at each other, and that we must not talk so much; but we talk to this very day.

Names and half-remembered faces people my mind with the past. Where did you go, and what did you see old playmates, old friends? And what do you do today?

The day wears on, and I decide to leave. There is little to see in the playground and nothing to do alone. But on another day, when there is no holiday, and the playground is filled with tumult, and the classrooms and corridors are alive with more than echoes, I shall come back, – for here I first heard the nightingale beauty of Keats; here Homer reached out and singed me with wonders that flamed wild from his realms of gold; here Wordsworth woke the spirit of the poet: from where such things occurred, one cannot be absent long.

Diffuse, Musician of the universe,
Your music's merry/mournful melodies
With Mercy's minion Mildness, and immerse
My mind in mist-mood mellow memories
Of music mingled magically with May
Most marvellous and all my moments most
Minute and meagre, marshalling away
Emotive musing – motioning almost
Emotion from my mind – that I might mould
My intermezzo mightiest amid
Immaculate materials manifold,
Mute mystery, mat, and marl, where meekly hid
Magnificence makes miracles, and more
Than miracles move moan-martyred, my encore!

The Letterbox

HALFWAY INTO THE HILLS, where the encroachment of the town is held back by the ever increasing wildness of the terrain, there is a labyrinth of lanes which leads to farms and sundry dwellings which have weathered the hillsides for a century or more. It is in these lanes that the townfolk walk on spring and summer evenings, at weekends, and on holidays; in fact, whenever the time and the weather are propitious for an escape from the confines of crowded streets and the ceaseless hub of urban life, these lanes are loved and lingered-along by all who search for peace and gentle pleasance, and do not wish to travel far.

Only I have travelled far, from childhood to the present day, through half a lifetime's wanderings here and there. It was a long journey, and often hazardous, although when I reflect it seems that the road I travelled was only a straight unerring path which would lead me back to where I began; as though the whole of my journey had been made through a maze whose exit and entrance were the same, and whose central object was not the end but merely the halfway point from and to my home.

Although the air is charged with the glory of spring, there is no-one here as I walk past the last bastions of the town and turn the corner into the narrow winding lane in which my dreams stumbled, strayed and idled even in my absence. Now I greet those dreams and embrace them as long-lost friends, holding them close until they vanish – merged into the inspiration of present thought.

On my left stands an old cottage with white walls and a low thatched roof. It is beautiful almost to the point of unreality, quaint and charming with its well-tended lawn and beds of Maytime flowers. It is my first sight of this cottage. Of course I was always aware of its existence, but until today I had never seen it; only the tall wooden gate which leads to the path which leads to the cottage door, and the ivy-clad stone wall which surrounds the garden are familiar to me.

But it is not the cottage which interests me, and I turn away from looking into the garden and look to the other side of the lane where a high half-brick and half-stone wall shuts off the lane from the bales and barns of a neighbouring farm. Yes, it is still there! Level with my chest a letterbox is fixed into the stones; rusted with age, there is no flapper at the opening to prevent its being the repository of the debris of the seasons and the home of insect throngs. – Perhaps too in this small niche there are leaves from the ivy on the other side of the lane. – Perhaps even the skeletal remains of those leaves which I posted into the wall when I was a child and knew that this was a fairy postbox, and that if I posted ivy leaves into it, and closed my eyes and wished, the wish would come true.

What became of those dead wishes? I try to remember those I had made when I posted my leaves, and whether or not they were granted. But I am unable.

Because I have journeyed to my beginning, I pick two leaves from the garden wall, carry them across the lane, kiss them, and close my eyes as I post them into the box and wish – a wish which already has been granted.

Oh for an age of spring, that I might pour
Liberation to my Lord, and with each vein
Bleed adoration all my life, and awe
Swell out my soul, and I my Lord sustain
With such as which he feeds me daily fare –
Fair season and the fathering-forth of things
Lovely to greater loveliness, – and bear
Him beauty back from whom all beauty springs.
Oh for such age, that dying I might live
In serving sweet my Lord while earth and sky
Are charged with heaven's ecstacy and give
Replenishment to life and, living, die
To live and die in springtime without end,
To pour libation when my Lord should send.

The Reservoir

ABOVE THE TOWN there is a reservoir which is so old that living memory cannot recall the time when it had been less than half-reclaimed by Nature, and since the frogspawn-dabbling, tadpole-tickling days of my childhood a score of successive generations of wild flowers have germinated, blossomed, withered and seeded along its banks, in an endless cycle of life, death and rebirth.

Once again it is the time of blossoming, daisies and dandelions, celandines and stitchworts jewel the deep lush grass which over-flows the banks and spreads its verdant vernal carpet over the adjoining fields. The surface of the water ripples as a light spring breeze wafts down the hillsides cool with the memory of last year's heather-glory, – as a Mayfly myriad, faery, ephemeral, dance and dive and die.

It is good to sit here; to sit and see, and sense the soul that animates the day; to pause awhile from life – and live.

I sit on a smooth-hewn stone, long-fallen from the granite walls which once protected the reservoir from the encroachment of the fields. As I sit, I pick at the lichen patterns on the stone, pull at the grass around me, feel the caress of coming summer on my face, and am suddenly overcome with an aching – an intense longing to become part of everything which surrounds me. It is an aching with which I have long been familiar, a dear and noble pain whose absence does not heal but wound: a pain for which there is no alleviation.

The burden of beauty is so great that no one soul can bear it, and in my sweet-suffering I recall other occasions in which the encountering of Nature's majesty has proved too much for my human clay.

For a while I close my eyes, half-unsensed by sensation and reverie, but the lowing of cows in a nearby meadow wakes me back to the world. For old time's sake I make a daisy chain and, as there is no one at hand to crown, fling it onto the water where it floats first one way and then another until it finally comes to rest beside a bed of reeds.

I peer into the shallow waters and watch a score of tiny creatures scurrying hither and thither among the pebbles at the bottom; I see a face reflected in the waters, but it is not mine. It is the face of a child which looks back at me, a child with laughing eyes who smiles, whose visage is healthy and incorrupt. I bend down to kiss it, but as my lips touch the water the vision dissipates, and the mirror becomes clouded with disturbed sediment.

Call me not man, for man I would not be
If in the name of man I – man – preclude
The joys of Nature from the sovereignty
Of my delight, and trade the fragile mood
Of innocence for knowledge, love and lust,
And leave the vastness of the poetic wild
For prosaic-pretty gardens. Though I must
Run with the years, let me remain a child.
If not in body, then within my heart,
Let childhood be the compass of my days,
And fill my soul with every glorious part
Of this so lovely world: let all my ways
Mix with the budded charm of youth and spring:
Child I was born, and to that state I cling.

The Forest

THE ROAD THROUGH the forest is steep and straight, and where the crumbling low granite walls are no longer in evidence it is banked by bramble, heather and bilberry whose bushes spill down to the road like billowing snowdrifts. The road is wet, water has seeped onto it from hill, field, and forest, from a thousand secret springs; but although the surface is damp it is even and well-constituted for this is no half-tamed forest trail but a road built to enable traffic to come and go from the town below to the isolated hill villages above. What it is not, is a road for pilgrims and wanderers, and as soon as I am able to find an opening in the bank I climb through and plant my feet on the moist floor of the forest.

Here the ground is softer, more treacherous to the walker and yet infinitely more pleasant, for beneath the sole of the shoe there is nothing to separate man from the mothering might of Nature. At first I am aware only of the silence, but soon I hear a multitude of sounds; the damp moss as it gives beneath my feet, squelching and oozing winter's melted snow and the showers of March and April; the urgent flutter of wing among pine; the free songs of the forest birds; the distant bleating of sheep and lambs on daisy-strewn hillsides; the sound of my own voice: until this very moment I have been aware that I have broken into spontaneous song.

What I sing I know not; certainly the music is familiar, strains of Mozart pour from me, *Figaro* and *The Magic Flute*; strains too, of Beethoven and Dvorak, and above all the wild and passionate last movement of Bruch's *Violin Concerto*. But the words are strangers and I ask myself in what language I sing, and to what these strange words pertain.

The words pertain to the overwhelming joy that is in my heart, to a joy which can be expressed by music but never by formal words

17

– for in what language and in what combination of tongues can we ever express emotion? The greater the need for expression, the more inadequate becomes the vocabulary of the tongue: there are simply not enough words: language is yet in its infancy. – And I defy the most accomplished polyglot to convince me that the sum total of the world's languages has power of interpretation sufficient enough to express or communicate any worthy idea or concept to its infinite degree: and emotion is infinite, – and I sing in the language of love.

But as soon as I become conscious of my singing it ceases, for I am struck by the notion that joy and love can only be best expressed unconsciously, before awareness imposes its barrier; love flows purely only where its course is unhindered. Later, when there is no time for thought, the song will rise again.

I walk silently past remnants of old cottages which are so ravaged by time and clime and the all-reclaiming forces of Nature that they are hardly even ruins. I walk in no direction but that of the moment's whim, and yet not wholly without purpose because this is a pilgrimage and although the destination has not been revealed the journey is sure and certain, for it was planned at the moment of my conception.

Mud, compacted with grass and pine-needles, cakes my shoes and is transferred to my trousers; my shoes leak, and my coat is snagged and torn by brambles and branches; but, rather than regretting this attack upon my person, I rejoice that I bear love's wounds.

Soon my pockets become filled with fir-cones and stones, mementoes of the day, later to be put away carefully and sometimes examined when a bout of deep nostalgia troubles my daily life. My wallet is a repository of leaves, some to be sent to far off friends as tokens of my affection, others to remain there until they disintegrate and the fragments fall away unnoticed.

As I penetrate its depths, the forest grows dark, for even though it covers not one tenth of the area of its mediaeval prime it is still yet deep and vast and provides a vital lung for the town, a place for the soul to rest, and – for the pilgrim, among its unordered ways and infrequent remains of civilisation – a paradise.

Latent too long, unleashed the greenworld grows
Gathering greatness like a raging fire
Quenchless throughout creation, quickening flows
Of forest grass in fields; and urging higher,
And yet still higher, luscious among leaves,
Buds lengthening to blossom-burst and break
A second age of beauty that enwreathes
The earth. The very stones seep life and wake
Their ancient sleep with moss and lichen wound,
And all the air is moist, the mountainsides –
Verdant in valleys – merge with mists; around
The woodland and the meadows torrent-tides
Of sap pour pure liquidity through days
Fertile to overfullness as they blaze.

The Hills

DRYSTONE WALLS line the roads which wind through meadows and moorlands and over the hills and far away as the eye can see. In their sheltering coltsfoots are still flowering, for here the seasons take no regard of calendar months but start and finish as they please. It has been a long wintering on the hills, in the upper hollows patches of snow are still lying, and in the fields lambing-time has only recently begun. But today the season has finally caught up with the month, and although still several weeks behind the advancement of the blossom and beauty of the lowlands, spring is here and walks in the fields of May.

All around me is music, the song of trickling water sings softly in the grass, the skylark climbs high and pours out a cascade of notes which tumble from heaven to earth. From distant woods the mellow cooing of pigeons wafts faintly on the breeze, ewes on the hillsides bleat caution to their leaping lambs who incautiously bleat back, from nowhere a cuckoo sings. All is music and all is life, and the newborn watch me from every side.

I fill my lungs with the clear pure air and sing as I breathe the blest breath of heaven. My singing joins that of the world but does not blend with it, for there is no natural human sound but that of laughter and crying, neither of which are appropriate to the moment. But I sing to express my joy, and hope that it does not offend.

Below me the town lies diminished by distance, and I scan over it to the plain beyond which eventually surrenders its flatness to a chain of mountains standing mysterious in the haze of the horizon. But I am in the hills, and it is to the hills I look as I follow the road that winds.

The higher winds the road, the harder howls the wind and the nearer the world is to winter. Pools of water, in what were once quarry chasms, ripple in the wind as dry dead brittle winter grasses rustle noisily around them; but the water sparkles in the sunlight, and is so clear that every pool becomes the looking-glass of heaven.

The wind buffets across the moors and bellows in billowing blasts, driving my footsteps faster and faster until suddenly I am running down the day, wild as the wind itself. Round every corner another vista opens, valleys and hills stretch endlessly into the deepening day. At last the road swoops down, and sheltered from the wind I pause and catch my breath in the calm of a valley, speaking to the sheep feeding there as I rest before beginning my slow ascent of the other side.

I walk leisurely now, too deep in thought for joy to animate me more. My thoughts range with the hills and valleys and have no purpose in their journeyings, but they are kind thoughts, and satisfying.

At the top of the hill a gate leads into the fields; here I lean against the wooden posts and look aimlessly at the day which soon will draw to a close.

Sheep are moving down the hillsides, dogs from the farm are gathering them in; soon I shall be gathered in too, and safe in the fold of the herded night. But not today, for I am on a pilgrimage, and in such there is no night.

There is a tenderness in the evening skies,
There is a peace which over all the earth
Falls softly and shuts up the weary eyes
Of all create. So has it been since birth,
That in the tranquil hush of those few hours
Which gently tie the night-time to the day,
My mind has breathed a balm that summer flowers
Can only breathe in million-blossomed May:
A balm that soothes the thought, and dulls the sense
To things unlovely, and to lovely things
Adds deeper loveliness in evidence
Of unseen truth. No longer sadly sings
My soul to leave the iron chains that bind
Its being to the mortal tragedy
Of human flesh, now – as day's strifes unwind –
Unwind the shackles of captivity,
And for a space its wings can roam at will.

The Valley

OVER THE HILLS and far away from the sight of human habitation, I have come to the valley of memories where time stands still and only my own song and the chorus of Nature disturb the silence of the day.

Weary after my long walk, I sit on the bridge along which the road crosses the valley and vanishes high among the tree-covered hills on the other side. Below me runs the river, wide and fresh from its clear mountain springs, downward dashing to meander in the lush meadows of which it is now almost in sight.

The bridge is so situated that it divides the valley in two, on the north side the terrain is mighty with the grandeur of mountain and wild moorland, but on the south side the landscape is soft and mild, opening gently to fields of pastoral loveliness. With beauty on either side of me I am hard pressed to decide on which side of the valley I should commence my wandering. I elect to take the more strenuous first, and climb over the gate by the end of the bridge and into the meadows that lead to the moors.

This northern side of the valley has ever been strange to me; no matter the countless number of times I have roamed its uplands, I have only been able to see my surroundings through the dim mists of legends and lore which have so filled up my mind with ancient days that the present has always seemed vague and unreal.

Even today, though I pause by the orchids in the wet grass, and kneel down to the mountain pansies on the hill, though the sheep tracks through the darkling heather and the greening fern are familiar, and the ancient rocks are comrades of old, the air belongs to the ancients, and the beauties and dreams to long ago.

I leave the mountains and moorlands to their mysteries, and after returning to the bridge where I eat the food which I have brought with me to sustain me through the day, I step into the sweet mildness of the southern half of the valley.

Here there is nothing strange; if the ancients do indeed haunt the upper part of the valley, then here they surely keep strictly within its confines all that is rich and fertile, charged with life and joyous beneath the sun. Fields beyond fields ascending softly into hills flow from the riverside and into the skies above. Trees fringe the river banks, beneath them grow violets, and the deep woods are dusky and thick with the haze of bluebell clouds. Here is a place for singing, and I sing to embrace the world!

Memory sings with me, not her usual and plaintive song, but a song that is vital and young. Our voices blend well, and as our singing fills the valley we are suddenly no longer alone. A throng of people walk in silent procession towards me; friends of my childhood and youth, acquaintances and intimates with whom I have been happy in these fields: as they draw level with me I notice that each bears the appearance he bore when last we were here together. They greet me with smiling eyes, as one by one they once more walk into and out of my life, until I am once more alone.

Golden and glorious, the shadow of my soul burns bright in my eyes, and drowns in the depths of my tears.

A certain sense of thankfulness is mine:
The river, and the meadow, and the wood –
The valley – wears a beauty as divine
As Paradise: the ground on which I stood
In childhood is unchanged, and once again
A child I walk the footsteps that I trod
When Innocence was mine. Oh, once again
The soul is mine that rests its wings in God.

The Village

As I step of the bus which brought me from the town of my early childhood to the village of my youth, I am brimming with excitement. Even before the bus came to a halt by the village green it had passed more than a dozen houses and farms whose occupants I knew by name, and now as I alight my brain whirls with expectation. – Who shall I see, and what shall we talk of? What has been changed, and what has remained unaltered?

The bus draws away and I stand and look around me at: the inn which is painted white and flourishes a newly-painted sign; the washing white and wholesome blowing in the fresh country air on the lines in the gardens of a row of terraced cottages; the heaped-up and scattered-overall-disorder of castings, rusted iron and cart-wheels in the yard of the smithy; new houses risen behind the inn where once a field lay waterlogged and low in the very centre of the village.

The smith waves to me, and I wave back; we say hello and nothing more, for to do so would be to break beyond the bounds of the relationship we established a lifetime ago.

How green it all is! Willows graceful in new leaf, gardens with lawns neat-trimmed and tidy, bushes in bud and bloom, oak and ash and rowan decked out in the season's best!

I pay my first visit, drinking tea and eating cake, cosy by the fire of an old lady. Frail and faltering now, she is strong and brave in warmth and kindness, and it is not without difficulty that I am able to excuse myself for not staying longer; but before I leave I am made familiar with the progress of all the members of her large family and acquainted with all that is current in the village's affairs, and we regret that the old hall has been demolished. I vow to call on her again before I leave.

As I close the cottage gate behind me, I am hailed by the church-warden whose long unheard voice seems as familiar as the day is new; we exchange greetings, and in a handful of words I present him with the history of my absent years.

I walk on and up the lesser of the two roads on which the village stands, past houses and cottages where remembered forms move fleetingly behind the windows; some see me and wave; others, unnoticing, go busily about their daily cares.

At last I reach a gate through which I have walked a thousand times. It leads through a garden porch where a hand-written notice confirms that the visitor knows where the key is kept that will let him into the house. I smile with satisfaction as I find the key in the same unsecret niche in which it has always hung. How trusting they are in the country!

I let myself into the house unnecessarily, for my approach has been seen through the windows by those who await within, and as I open the door I am met by those I love, whose voices are accent-less, whose faces are dear, and whose hearts are as my own. And instantaneously I cease to be a visitor; and the village embraces its son.

Wise was I once, and innocent, unweaned,
White as the robes that wound me, being bound
By no man's curse or mercy fathering, free
To habit heaven; whole was I, profound
In untaught truth; grace grew me; well I knew
The company of angels, other light
Than earth's pale glory gilded me and threw
A radiance on all my seeing, – sight.
Wise let me be once more, new worth to wear
The beauty of my birthright, simple, sure,
Pure in its light's bright seeing, being heir
To bliss whose breath is breathed by no man's law
But that of God, or – unreformed – deny
That once was light, and this light lose thereby.

The Lane

IN MID-SPRING before the warmth of the sun has dried the April showers from the grass, the lane that leads from the main road and ends in a farmyard is always particularly wet; whether or not this is because it bears no sign of having been made by man, I cannot say. All I can say is that the mud and puddles are in greater evidence here than in any other of the village lanes, Today the sun is shining, but although I feel its kind and gentle caress it does little to dry the ground beneath my feet and thus, whilst looking at the hedgerows on either side of me, I do not let my eyes wander away too often from where I am walking.

The lane is long and narrow; curving down softly from the village to a farm whose fields lie lush and green by the river. It is a lonely, gentle lane, no traffic but the farmers' cars and tractors disturbs its silence, and in consequence Nature has been very happy to make it one of her most treasured homes and has furnished it with great prodigality.

Passing an ancient kissing-gate through which egress can be made to the ruins of the old rectory and its long-vanished gardens, I reach the first bend; there I pause and turn around to catch my last glimpse of the village; from now on all will be only green and glorious.

The fields on either side of the hedges are trampled by a herd of cows who look at me with momentary curiosity over the shoulder-high hawthorn which will soon be embraced by sweet-blossoming honeysuckle. I greet them and they show no surprise.

Continuing, I see the first farm ahead of me; before I reach it the banks of the hedge rise higher and I search among the grass to see if I can discover any eggs which the hens may have laid there. How happy I would be if I could find one and take it to the farmer's wife in part-reparation for those I found and proudly took home with me when I was a child and knew no other than that the eggs and the hens which laid them were as free as my own spirit. But there are none. However, I am delighted to see that the wood-sorrel still grows here, and I pluck a sprig of it and put it in my shirt and hold it to my heart.

Through the farmyard, past the shippons, the lane advances deep-mudded and oozing, as barking dogs run round me and leap up to lick my hands. I say hello to them and talk for a while to the farmer who has come out of a barn to ascertain the cause of the commotion. He talks to me as if I were still the neighbour who lived in the cottage a field away from his door; and a lifetime is passed in a moment.

Now the lane eases in its descent and the pastures begin to open up on either side. I walk slower and slower for I must not hurry my pleasure but relish every moment. But suddenly I find I have made greater progress than I intended, so lost have I been in reverie that for some time I have been looking only into myself. I retrace my steps some 75 yards and focus on the outside world again. Here there are bugle, campions, stitchworts, bluebells, celandines and violets. As no one is there to witness, I bend and kiss them, and feel them kiss me back as they trace their globuled moisture on my lips.

A few yards ahead of me is a gate through which the lane passes for a short distance at the end of its course before it reaches the farmyard. I walk up to it, past the fading daffodils which the farmer's wife has planted there and, as I lean against the wooden bars, horses gallop towards me, dogs bark, cows low, the fowl in the farmyard cluck and hiss and gobble, and beauty ravishes me on every side as I lift my eyes to the distant hills, and turn silently to bless the hallowed ground on which I stand.

How is it there at night? What dreams awake
Among the leaves, and all along the lane
Echo the fled day's dalliance and ache
For rest and – restless – ache for rest again?
How is it told by starlight? What desires
Mad in dark shadows move? What passions wreak
Havoc in sunless heaven? What strange fires
Beneath the midnight burn? What senses seek
Requitement in the deep thick hush that forms
The gentle folded many-curtained night?
How is it there when moonlight's mystery storms
The firmament with spears of spectral light?
How is it there outside my seeing? – Keep
The hedgerows there safe haven whilst I sleep?

The Farm

AS I PICK my way through puddles and walk onto the firmer but
even muddier surface of the farmyard, I am overwhelmed by the
reception that is given to me. Two dogs fly out of nowhere, yelping
and bouncing, bristling and wagging, finally slinking and skulking
with heads hung low in suspicious curiosity as they circle me from
a comfortable distance. Geese with outspread wings spit and hiss
as they run past me, hens fluster, guinea-fowl gurgle, horses whinny
in the stables, a bull bellows from afar, and sundry cats – half-
hidden among milk churns and bales of straw – eye me with silent
contempt.

But I am only disconcerted for a moment, for as suddenly as
the clamour began it comes to an end and calm is restored to the
farmyard. Bereft of her mate, who has sped to the fields, the
sheepdog wags cautiously towards me and licks my hand as if to
give me the entree to the yard, and in two minutes we are established friends.

Although I feared that the tumult of my reception would bring
forth the occupants of the farm, no one appears, and I am able to
explore the outbuildings and chicken-runs at my leisure. Whilst I
am glad that the occupants are as yet unaware of my presence, it
has not been my intention to come and go without having met and
talked with them, but that is for later; now I am happy to wander
alone and let thoughts and impressions come to me freely, unin-
fluenced by conversation, however pleasant, with my fellow man.

My wandering brings me joy. In the orchard-paddock all remains
untidy and haphazard, no innovation has been made during the
passing of the years; bricks, tyres, branches, nettles and weeds stand
on and in the grass as they have always done. Here and there nar-
cissi bloom palely while chickens and hens scratch and peck the
riches of the earth. The sheds in the chicken-runs are old and

dilapidated, but proof against the weather; I walk to them and greet the hens who cluck back to me as they brood.

In the cowsheds cows and calves press cold, damp, cavernous-nostrilled noses to my hand as I lean over the half-doors to see what they are about. There is something good in the smell of cows, and a feeling of comfort comes over me as they mingle their milch-breath with mine; there is peace in their deep dew-filled eyes, and sadness, and gentle reproach. I visit the horses in the stables, unlike the cows they do not stand motionless but pace about and nudge me with their huge heads, expectant of my touch in return.

Though all is in its ancient place, the barn in which I used to help the farmer collect the eggs from the battery-hens is now empty, and although I miss the opportunity of walking through and filling up a bucket to leave at the door of the farm, I am not sorry.

The farm door is opened to my knocking, and the farmer's boy, who is now a grown man and has not seen me for twenty years, welcomes me unsurprised, for to him there is nothing special about the day. He calls to the farmer and his wife who are drinking mugs of tea in the room to which I am led; they give me the same welcome and tell me to sit down. I choose a place on the couch where a lamb sits and raises its head in expectation of the milk whose bottle has been placed in my hand.

We talk of the past, of the life of the village and farm; and although reference is made to my long absence, I cannot bring myself to make mention of the travels and adventures through which I have lived since last here: for here, where remembrance merges with present day, they seem only to have been small and trivial episodes in an interrupted, half-forgotten dream.

Here let me lie the summerlong and sip
In these enchanted fields the matchless wine
That lulls the land with mildness from the lip
Of Paradise; all through the summershine
Drowsed let me dream daylong soothe in the shade
Of hedgerows heaped with blossoming, and keep –
Here where deep shadow silences invade
The shining grass – safe rest, and never sleep
But idly count cloud-clocks that tick the time
Of dandelion days when breeze bear –
Hallowed in half-breathed interludes – sublime
Musk fragrances that wanton on the air
As on the ocean rainbow-wreathéd foam, –
And heal my heartache for the heart of home.

The Wood

WHENEVER I FIND MYSELF in the barbaric position of having to trample-down nature in order that I may gain access to some desired goal, I become instantly aware of the beauty I am about to despoil, and am filled with such self-loathing that were I treading upon rose-petals my feet would feel only the piercing of thorns.

A few minutes ago as I climbed over the barbed-wire fence out of the field and into the wood, I once again felt the hurting beneath my feet. But it was not onto rose-petals which I had stepped but onto the young green shoots of a vast carpet of bluebells which covered the wood as far as they eye could see.

How they creaked and squelched beneath my feet, – those early witnesses of the coming of May's fullness – oozing sap as they were bent and broken by my footfall, some springing slowly back, others laid low forever. How I despised myself! And yet, I walked on, for wasn't this my wood, the wood in which I had spent a thousand days of childhood, the same wood whose memory had haunted the thousand thousand aching empty nights of my exile? Yes! – and I, if any, am entitled to tread down these shoots, my never failing love has earned the right; and yet, forgive me, oh forgive me darling joys!

Here and there some bluebells are already in bloom. Here too, a handful of campions blend their misty pink with the green and blue. Of all the hues of spring there are none which combine so well as those of the bluebell and pink campion; each a splendid bloom whether alone or in the company of its own kind, both gain an added loveliness when they blossom side by side: a loveliness which speaks of lengthening evenings, dusk and drowsy light. Below, where the wood drops down the hill and enters the swamp which bounds its realm, marsh-marigolds glow golden in the gloom, their fleshy leaves and stems large with spring, their burnished bowls irresistible as the sun itself.

Beloved wood! I know you so well, you are as dear and familiar to me as anything on the earth: your trees and flowers, swamps and rabbit warrens, your unfurling ferns and rich black soil are as they always were. You have not changed in any way. Only I have altered in the process of time. The child who daily sang and wandered in your embrace has become man, he has matured toward the fulfilment of his estate, and his heart has known other joys; others he has loved, and he has experienced sorrow, and can now hardly remember innocence. But he remembers you, as he has always done, no inch of you is a stranger to his eye, no fragrance unfamiliar. No sound, nor touch, nor rustling among leaves is your's which has not haunted him all the days of his absence.

– Thus it was I mused as I trampled down the season's sweetest, step by step, until I walked to where last year's cluttered and ravaged bramble-wreck lay brown and battered, half-holding me fast as I left the wood behind.

Crush not the fragile flowers
In over-zealous passion,
For love with haste may overlook
The splendour of the leaves,
And love of flowers just deceives.

And love of ostentation is
A love without perception,
Not understanding, seeing
Only obvious being.

Hidden 'neath the trumpet-blast,
The drums, the fire, the screaming,
'Neath gloss, and gross, and glitter,
Hides the beauty unseen yet –
And worldly eyes with ease forget.

The Ridge

AS IT SHOULD BE, all is as it was. Nothing is changed. The peace is inviolate and nothing breaks the noiselessness but the pulse of the day and the inner-music which floods my being. Here is the fusion of past and present, where all is timeless and changeless; where I have felt at one with all: a part of all I sense, and all I sense a part of me, where only the silence roars.

I walk aimlessly through short and dewy grass, stopping now and then to drink in the vast beauty which engulfs me, my head throbbing with joy; suddenly I am timeless too.

Past and present: the being I am now is one and indivisible. Here what I was, I am; what I am, I will be; only here is this experience made so clearly manifest. It is as though I were born solely to be here, and that all other stages of my life have been merely incidental to the predestination of my presence here. For this is very heaven.

Before me the long high ridge drops steeply to an expanse of green pastureland on whose damp grass horses, sheep and cattle feed and sleep. In the centre of the pasture is a small pond, beyond which an irregular line of trees bounds the irregular course of the river: my river. I watch the motion of the day, shapes and shadows gliding among the fields; I look down to the farm, the picture-book-pretty farm whose land this is, and I voice my blessing upon its occupants.

Beyond field and river and farm the land lifts, eventually rising sharply to form the promontory which dominates the landscape and beckons to all who live under its shadow to climb its heather heights.

To my right the wood tumbles toward the farm, and terminates in a swamp a short distance from the outbuildings. Behind me lie dark windswept fields which in a few months will bask golden in the glory of the grain. But it is to my left that the view is most lovely, it is one of panorama, woods, fields, farms, churches and roads stretch out in a haphazard patchwork, fading into the blue and misty hills which rise mass beyond mass on the horizon.

Beloved spot! Dearest of all my joys! As much as I stand in you now, so you have stood within my heart these many years, calling me to you, wounding me with joy, ever there. Sometimes I have cursed you, how many times has remembrance of you disturbed my daily life? Where may I not have settled but for you? To what purpose may I have lived my life?

But even as I rage, the answer is given to me as for a brief moment I hear earth and heaven together singing. . . . 'To none, but to be here'. And I am humbled.

He kissed me, and the moistures of his mouth
Made summer for my soul, I felt the sun
Wintering within me waken, sudden south
Soothe in me surge; I dared communion
Of flesh with sacrament; I felt the fire
Of heaven in my heart, and in his flame
I flourished fearless quenched of all desire
But to endure the death; he overcame
My being, he was Eucharist that fed
My universe with radiance of more
Than glory's mere immaculate; he bled
Love in my veins, and beauty beyond awe
Of adoration in my spirit – wine
That bruised my lips with dews of the divine.

The Hollow

THERE IS A CERTAIN HOLLOW in the hill in which, in all the years I have known it, and for which I most rejoice, I have never seen either track or trace of any other human visitation. It is because this spot is so apparently devoid of humanity that I have elected it my own, a secret sanctuary over which I enjoy proprietorial right, a tiny realm over which I am lord and master.

Two sides of the hollow are bordered by gorse bushes entangled with a confusion of blackberry stems half-undermined by rabbit-burrows whose unseen inhabitants, at the first hearing of my song, have already long-since hidden themselves. The third side of the hollow is a grassy bank, here and there interspersed with molehills, stones, daisies, dandelions and twigs, and is of a nature very much consistent with that of the field into which it opens.

But it is the fourth side, the ridge side of the hollow, which is my favourite. Here a group of dark alder trees rises up from the boggy ground (for the hollow acts as a natural reservoir for water which seeps and oozes down from the ridge) and spreads its black branches in spectral silhouettes against the sky. At the foot of the trees, pale and fragile in the rich black soil and deep green fullness of the grass, are scattered an array of primroses – among the first I have seen this year.

The songs I had sung as I walked down the hill are ended, and careless of my clothes I kneel on the grass and trace my fingertips gently around the flowers which are so delicate that I can hardly feel them. I touch each petal and breathe upon it unspoken bene-diction, the salutation of my love. How perfect is the primrose, so light and fragrant is scent, so fair and fragile to behold!

Every springtime when I have walked in these fields I have hurried here to see the primroses, they have never failed me but have always been here, patient and smiling as if in wait for my approach. On former occasions I have refrained from picking them, but today they call out for me to love them not with the love of the adorer but with the love of a lover: yet even so, I am loth to manifest my love in an action which can only destroy. But even as I ponder my dilemma, I realise that to refuse the primroses, for the sake of the preservation of my finer feelings, would be to deny them the answering of their love. This I cannot do. Who loves me shall be loved in return.

I pluck two of the flowers, hold them to my face, press them to my eyes, my cheeks, my nose, and my lips. I smell their breath, and taste their warm and gentle kisses tendering on my mouth; I shake the dew-pearls from their yellow eyes, and let them fall on mine.

Oh Spirit whose life sustains, whose home is in the earth and in the sky, who is the heart of all, whose being in all is all, in whom is all, my communion, take of my love as my love takes of your's!

Reverently, lovingly, I feed on the flowers; and, satisfied, take my silent leave.

How can it be, in all the wealth of flowers,
That one alone awakes such thoughts in me
That make me in mad-magic-midnight hours
Rise from dead dreams, and the uncertainty
Of sleep to keep a lover's rendezvous
Deep in soft petals, soft I've often kissed
In ecstacy, to feel again the true
Sweet-centred love around my senses twist:
Lying deep in deep-yellow, deep within
Veil-frail pale-yellow, deep until I sink
To think of nothingness, – nor think it sin
To tremble on the barren-bosomed brink
Of mortal being to immortal state,
Till sense unsensed, no longer sense can sate.

The River

As I CLIMB through the barbed-wire and slide down the steep and muddy bank, snatched-at by branches and clawed and cut by briars, I slither and stumble a score of times before reaching the little stream which runs quick and silver at the bottom. I pause there awhile, and as I bend down to look at the bottom of the stream where the golden saxifrage blossoms are submerged, I let the water wash away the thick mud which has accumulated on my wellingtons.

Pulling myself up from the stream with the aid of an alder branch which hangs conveniently low, I push my way through leaves and twigs, nettles and brambles, and the debris of a thousand floods until finally I reach the pebbles lying white and grey and speckled, freckled at the river's edge.

Now I stop and look around me through a field of butterbur, their pink stems standing sentinel and seeding above fast flourishing rhubarb-like leaves; soon their flowers will have fallen, and until the end of summer the leaves will be umbrella-huge, providing yet more obstacles along the wanderer's way to the river.

The air is cool and filled with the odour of wild garlic which grows dainty and white in thick rich leafy abundance all around; but here the heart of Nature is warm, and every year spring blossoms two weeks earlier by the river than in the nearby woodlands and fields.

It is still only the middle of May, but here already the wood-anemones have nearly all faded from the fair company they keep with bluebells and pink campions which are at their height of loveliness: however, I manage to find two which are still in their pale white fragile prime; I pick them and cast them into the river, my sacrifice to the day and to the unseen spirit whose mighty presence breathes enchantment and through whose enchantment I dream.

I search among the pebbles for those flat stones best suited for playing 'ducks and drakes', and to my great delight find that I have lost none of my skill as I make the stones bounce high or low across the water, which ever way I choose. Here the river runs rapidly, and over the years has changed its course several times, an occurrence which is evidenced by the variously shaped indentations of the banks, and the small and pebble-strewn islets which are as yet un-invaded by seedlings and sand.

Farther along the water is both deep and shallow, but by drop-ping stones into it and listening to the tones of the resulting splashes, I am able to gauge the depths and discover how best I can cross to the other side; but having discovered the best way, I do not take it – preferring to walk farther along the shore with which I am most familiar.

And I wander away the day, deep in my love of the river and the music of its waters, passionate in my love of the life along its banks. Through marsh and stream, over torn-up roots and branches, I tread quietly, giving no voice to the song which I sing.

Although the contours of the banks embrace many shapes, and many islands and islets have surfaced and sunk since the days I lived close enough to visit the river almost daily throughout my years, its lifepulse is little changed. Still the water flows on and on, sometimes deep, sometimes shallow, now quickly and clattering over stones, now loitering languid in fathomless pools; resting and restless, racing and lingering, it is yet my river, and bleeds in my blood as it courses its life to the sea.

Wild winds the stream dawn-dewy meadows pearled,
Past purple moors, and mothering presently
Milch-pastures pleasant, widens in a world
Of pastoral nonpareil, and languidly
Lies leisured there slow motion breathing shade
Of willowwood and alder, fern and fall
Fragrant drowsed down to dogrose frail in fade
From glorious to ghost-glory, green and all
The shadowlight of summer – till the sun
Of summertime itself it sees, and then
Surging from softness sudden is begun
Bright under boughs the whirling wild again.

The Field

FOR AS LONG AS I CAN RECALL, whenever I have spoken of some remembered joy with particular affection, people would tell me not to be a dreamer – that the beauty of which I spoke was based on nostalgia and sentimental fantasy, and that reality would prove how well I had been deceived. Such words annoyed me twofold. Firstly, because I disliked the arrogant assumption that the status of the dreamer should be directly equated to that of the fool, and secondly, because those very people who were so free in their unsought opinions had had neither sight nor experience of the joy of which I spoke and which was so dear to me.

Today I walk through a field whose memory has been one of such particular and deep joy that I have never spoken of it, holding the vision pure in my mind, inviolate from outward siege.

As I walk, a deeper joy than remembered floods through me, a joy that is real and undreamed, and being so is boundless – for even dreams have bounds. I pause and stand enraptured, listening to the magical songs of May; the swish and flutter of sapphire-darting swallows swooping in mad arcs from heaven to earth and back again, pigeons cooing soothly among trees, vigilant ewes bleating to their gambolling lambs abounding, the thunder-thudding tread of shire horses ambling slowly down from the farm, the mighty river rolling and rumbling on its course through Nature's heart. No, this could never be a dream, one awakes from a dream – but to this, one awakes.

Although the leaves are not yet on the trees, a billion buds are bursting, eager for even the least blush-burning kiss of the early sun, and although leafless the trees are green. In the hedgerows the blackthorn is no longer bare but is covered with a veil of white as

47

if she were a bride in waiting for her groom the Lord of May; flowerless the hawthorn buds are blossoming, and already I have been able to eat one or two of those nurseling leaves my father called Adam's bread. The whole world is waking in this small field, a myriad gnats dance and mingle by the river's edge, daisies lift their yellow eyes to the sun, kingly dandelions parade their gold among the green, and the very ground seems pulsing with the beat of life.

I am not alone in this enchanted spot. As I passed through the farmyard I made friends with a dog who followed me to the field; he walks and runs by my side, through and around my legs, eager and young with no thought in his head for he is a wise dog and like his grandfather who would also accompany me here, neither dreams nor cares to dream of dreams, for what he knows is all to him and he needs nothing more.

Especially at lambing-time I take
My tangled thoughts (mark how the rosebriar
mimes)
And turn taut twists of sentiment to make
From madness, measured, teased-out, tangled
rhymes;
Some stumbling string wound words round buds
that spring
Intemperate to blossoming and bear
Mild-maiden glory on a moment's wing,
And waste their passion on the wanton air;
Some burgeoning breed beauty among shifts
Of sun and shade, and through the interchange
Of day and darknight fail and fall in drifts
Autumnal, withered, worn where rough winds
rage;
Others – such one is this – brood but to lie
Long-rooted in the fields of memory.

The Storm

THE WEATHER FORECAST predicted heavy rain and thunderstorms, and certainly the sky is leaden and the air hangs still and brooding as I walk along the river bank. But I am determined in my mind and, come storm with strife and fire among the heavens or floods from the deep oceans of the sky, I shall not abandon my walk and my intentions of the day.

The fields are silent, and the animals of the farm are mute and motionless, those of the wild fled at my coming, and neither song nor fluttering of feather betrays the hidden presence of the birds. But for my singing, and the river's deep undying music which accompanies my song, there is silence in all the world.

The warmth of the afternoon surrenders to a sudden coldness which chills the air, but the fall in temperature – rather than refreshing – combines unpleasantly with the heavy skies and makes the threatening atmosphere seem even more oppressive. In the distance I hear the low rumble of thunder, but it is as yet too far away to break the silence which is immediately around me, and I continue to sing as the sky darkens and glowers closing the day in sudden night. But soon the first pattering of rain adds its light staccato song to mine as it falls on the trees and the grass and dances on the river, spinning circles in the flow which grow ever closer to each other as the shower increases in strength and the thunder-rumble of the clouds booms ever nearer.

Sheets of lightning flash from the west, and at last I grow uncomfortable in my position by the river, and search for a group of trees under which I can shelter until the storm is over. But I can find no trees nearby which could provide me with sufficient cover, and so I must go further along the river to where I know a tall group of hawthorn grows; it will protect me from the rain, and while I shelter beneath it I can sing and watch the rising of the water as the river floods new life.

The hawthorns have not yet broken into leaf and afford but scant protection from the deluge, and only by twisting and crouching am I able to manoeuvre my body to a position where it can stay relatively dry.

Lightning crackles, dazzles, thunder crashes, rain drives, and the world is boisterous and frantic with sound and light. Though my clothes are now becoming more and more sodden with each passing moment, and my general aspect is that of the well-bedraggled, my spirit soars, and I am filled with untameable elation – as though the whole of my being were joined to the force of the elements.

The song I have been singing is done, and now I sing a new song – not with my mouth but with my very essence, a song that is wild and free, inspired of itself, magnificent in its range, and glorious in its power. Wilder it sings, further and further from my corporate being it flies, on and on until the motion of the storm bears it away to share in its fierce journey of might made manifest.

With the storm dies the song, the skies clear, the music of the birds sounds sweet on every side, the fields give thanks for nourishment, and once again the air is animate with May.

But I will walk no further, I am cold and wet, and have no more to see.

The voice of heaven everywhere is heard;
It thunders among mountains; in the sea
White-throated waves swell out its tumult,
   stirred
By winter storms; it blossoms lyrically
Of summer's breath, – and at the dawn's first
   blush
Sings life in woodlands loud until the day
Scatters its loveliness; in evening's hush
It soothes the soul, and murmurs mild away
The martyred mind; it shapes our slumberings;
Its music animates our mortal clay;
Its mightiness throughout creation rings;
It rolls its roaring silence round the spheres
Like the thrummed drumbeat of thronged angel
   wings,
Pulsate with adoration's unfledged tears.

The Waterfall

I WALK THROUGH a dark tunnel of burgeoning leaves, down the steep incline of a lane which twists and turns in its descent from the main road to the valley below. On the right-hand side of the lane trees stand tall and gloom astride high banks on which the leaves of bluebells and dog's mercury vie to proclaim the definitive shade of green, whilst on the other side a half-fledged streamlet oozes through briars and trees less stark, and the ground glades more gently, mild and golden with great cupped marsh-marigolds.

As I walk I am aware of a distant rumbling; a rushing, crashing, rumbling which increases in volume as I continue towards its source. Suddenly the rumbling thunders, and the dark green tunnel gives way to hedgerows and my eyes are sharply assailed by the light bright white flash crash smash splash of the waterfall.

There is music in the thundering that unfolds; cadences, strains and threads of scattered melodies, music of life, and darker and deeper tones of power and force and might which bear along the lighter chords, and continue long after those chords have faded into nothingness. The music is hypnotic, from the first moment of its hearing, when in the distance the low murmurs and rumblings call the listener to come closer and hear the clang of its thunder in his heart, and feel the joy of its spray pattering wet upon his face. Closer to, the hypnotic quality is so greatly intensified that it becomes no easy matter to think that beyond the clamour of the waterfall exists any other sound.

But the water flows on, and rainbows illuminated by the fresh splendour of the spring sun leap and dance in the foam which bubbles and billows at the bottom of the weir; and there is happiness in my soul as I listen and watch the roaring cascades of water tumble and fragment.

I stand on the bridge underneath which the newly fallen water steadies itself and swells the flow which glides smoothly through butterbur and elder until it sweeps slowly out of view around a wide bend in its course, tired from its exertions, spent of its force of foaming froth and fury.

As I stand I am filled with wonderful knowledge: knowledge that this moment is unique, that the sound that fills my ear and the sight that fills my eye will never again be repeated – for the notes of the music are played once and never more; between their strands changes in the air, the breeze, the depth and speed of the water, an insect's wings, alters the pitch and the frequency; and leaves, twigs, branches, petals – all that is borne over the weir adds and subtracts to and from the theme of the watery song. Moment by moment, the power and angle of the sunlight changes, nuances of shadows play and stray in the falling water, pearls of foam blow hither and thither. The entire visual and audible nature of the waterfall is that of a kaleidoscope and constant mutation.

I came to the waterfall to revisit a scene of my youth, to see and hear that which thrilled my eye and ear in earlier years, and although the impulses of that which I had held changeless in memory have all been replaced, I am not disappointed for I realise that even in the days of my youth the reality was perfidious, and that I witnessed then what I witness now – not a scene of bucolic wonder imitating glimpses of heaven, but an ephemeral parade of sight and sound which ceases to exist even at the instant at which it is perceived.

But sensation is better than thought, and I turn away from my philosophical speculations and drink-in the beauty that is before me: the trees which overhang the river and on two sides frame the waterfall, the little island which comes and goes with the seasons and has once more placed its siting to where I knew it as a boy – soon its shingle surface will green with opportunistic life, until once again some future day's rainfall floods the river, submerging it the while.

Just now the whirling-white wild waterfall
Spun out a web of rainbow-threaded light
Bright as the crowned kingfisher's fleet flight,
  small,
Slight, frail as dewfall down from daisy height;
Unleashed it sprang, a second's space, and
  flung
A lustre on the lowly celandine,
And danced wild wood-anemones among
And – dancing – glanced them with its
  dazzling shine;
Breathless it blessed the butterbur, then flew
Fast from the world and left the dallying day
Far lovelier for the interlude that knew
Veiled heaven in the lifespan of the spray, –
While, left alone, mankind on every side
Strained sight to glimpse the mirror of its pride.

The Church

STANDING ON A LOW HILL a short distance away from the road, the church dominates the village as surely as if it had been built in its centre, for despite its location the church is indeed the centre around which the life of the village revolves. Except for the village hall which shelters under its wing, and the inn with which it shares a relationship of great cordiality, the church is the sole meeting point for the villagers; and that is as it should be in a small community where life is lived simply and the pure tradition which breathes household laws is untarnished by the spirit of the age.

I have walked into the church unknowing what to expect, and yet with the gentle conviction that no great change will have been wrought in its appearance, and I am more than gratified to find that nothing is changed at all.

The dark-stained pews are empty, and I walk to where I sat silent and simmering youth's rebellion, passive, each Sunday morning. There is no rebellion within me now, time has taught me acceptance and tolerance of the ways and needs of man, though not the ability to pay lip-service to creeds to which my conscience cannot subscribe wholeheartedly. Whether rightly or wrongly, I hold religion to be the most personal of all possessions, a matter between God and his creatures alone; if there is a mediator between the two, then for me that mediator is the conscience of the individual – more strict and chastening than all the articles of faith, but sadly, unlike God, merciless and unforgiving.

Silently I take my place in the pew, and as I sit motionlessly reflecting on days that are no more, a sudden light streams through the stained-glass windows and stirs the quiet air with sunbeams and kaleidoscopic colour, filling the church with choir and congregation with whom I take communion. The hymn of the morning rings loud, psalms and the Easter hymn, Harvest and Christmastide sing. Who knows them well knows heaven.

As quickly came the light, as quickly it vanishes, and with it the singers in whose midst I sang; but the song continues its music and sings in my soul as I quietly close the door behind me and enter the churchyard.

Here there is light and the singing of birds; there is no death where the dead are lying. I walk from grave to grave and read the names inscribed on the headstones; how many I know, how many I know no more! One after another old friends have been laid to rest; side by side unlikely bedfellows lie, but at peace and in safety at last.

By one grave I linger longest. It is the grave of my father. No headstone marks his resting place, no tended plants bloom over him; but his is the finest of all earthly places in which to lie, for Nature has scattered wild flowers there, and insects fly among them; birds sing in the grass that grows wild beside the sunken mound, and nothing lies between Heaven and earth but the air that is pure and clean.

From where I stand I can see my old home, and the window through which I would watch the church keep watch on the flowers of the field.

Most when the May's mild murmuring in my ear
Bears on its bluebell breath a Sabbath song,
Singing incipient summer, sun and clear
Wide open skies; frail-fragrant all along
The hedgerows drowsed dog-roses intertwined
With honeysuckle sweet, steeped beauty born
Daily in new burst buds to blossom kind
As that rich blood which wept a crown of thorn;
And dapple on green hillsides drifting sheep;
And rivers idling languid in the shade
Of silent trees – or glistening and aleap
With life; and life in robes of light arrayed;
Most then I sing the May that is in me
And – singing – sense creation's harmony.

The Cottage

THE LITTLE LANE that leads to the cottage is banked by daffodils golden and glowing in the deep grass behind which hawthorn hedges give half-hearted defence from the ever-threatening invasion of the fields. An unkempt strip of weed and grass runs down the centre of the lane, for it is so narrow that cars are only able to travel along it within the narrowest of confines, and consequently the middle has never known the despoliation of the tyre's heavy tread.

A gaunt and giant ash tree stands halfway down the lane; the bark is rough with age, and green with lichen and damp weather, and I have to run my hands over it for several minutes before I am able to trace the initial which I sawed into it during the first months of my residence at the cottage a generation ago. The letter has grown with the tree, and the cut is ragged and indefinite, but I have pleasure in finding its evidence of my former presence here.

Since I moved away various occupants have lived in the cottage, and although I have no knowledge of the present residents, I have determined to pay a visit and request admission and the freedom of the garden: both are granted.

So much has changed in the cottage that it is hard to recognise the home in which I lived longest of all, only the views from the windows have not changed.

As if in a yesterday of yore, I find that I have walked into the living-room and straight to the small window which looks eastwards over fields and far out to the distant, dreaming, mothering hills; from this window I have watched the passage of years, shades and shapes of shadows and seasons stealing noiselessly over the land-scape, filling my mind with visionary peace.

I am shown around every room, how strange that seems – and how strange is the feeling that so much of my life has been lived among alien walls. But walls and furnishings are only the skeletal parts of the building and between them is space for the unseen spirit to dwell, and it is with the spirit that I have most to do.

Having no substance the spirit does not change, and it reaches out to me with the comfortable love of a long and treasured friendship, placing within my grasp joys and sadnesses, encounters and conversations, music and words which the world's blind faring had long since stolen from me.

The spirit that dwells in the house dwells also in the garden, and as I stroll down the path all thrives as my father planted. I wander between lawns, through seasons of flowers, past beds of roses in red and yellow bloom, to where summer sun burns down: I sit among phlox and helenium writing poetry to the glory of the hour before the windy fruitfulness of autumn bends the apple trees low to the orchard floor, and old winter walks chill in the world, wrapped up tight in his blanket of ice and snow.

And again it is spring, in the dream of the moment I have lived through the life of the year.

I leave without looking back; there are many lives and many years, and each is the dream of a moment.

All that I longed for was a gentle home
Among green hills, and all the quiet joy
Of simple living, liberty to roam
The pastoral wide and leisurely employ
My mind in musing of the humble kind –
Not dreaming of great glory, but of light
Sufficient to inspire though not to blind
The frailty that is the human sight; –
And tranquil being inwardly, and in
The world outside to watch the sequence sure
Of season and new season flow within
The harmony of nature's moral law;
And in my gentle pleasance, peace of mind,
Safe sheltering, and hope of humankind.

Evening

IN THE AGONY of his red flames the sun dies into his grave behind the mountains which bound the west in a shadowy chain. It is evening, but although the sun is dying, the memory of his light will linger a few more hours on the hills before the deep night falls and earth is laid to rest.

I have come to the end of my pilgrimage, I have wandered among the dearly loved and visited shrines of the past, and now it is time to leave. Just one night lies before me, one last deep night in my love, and then with the waking day a deeper night will fall.

No sadness invades my soul as I walk up the hill to the house which has been the base from which my pilgrim days have been passed; my soul is too much filled with contentment for sadness to find its dwelling there.

How beautiful is the earth! How beautiful the song that sings from the hills in the evening air! The forest lies dusk before me; on the tops of the hills glimmer the first faint lights from unseen windows of houses lost on the moor; below me the village is hushed; and in the fields thick shadows prowl noiselessly in the realms of the darkening deep.

How beautiful is the earth! – the thought sings through me again and again, and I am filled with an elevated joy – mighty, yet calm as the tendering twilight itself.

How beautiful is the earth! – and how sweet are the joys it inspires, and in those joys what tears!

How beautiful is the earth! – and how beautiful are the tears which mingle and move in a melancholy more sweet than common joy!

It is over, night has fallen and the sounds of the night have banished the songs of the day, but only from the world have the songs been banished, for the song that lived in me lives on, and sings in the sleep of my years.

Who shares with me this Maynight shelters me
In shades of peace, the harsh unholy day
Is laid to rest; who shelters shares with me
More than the night, – light nuance, interplay
Of shape with shadow; low in nursling leaves,
Sounds in a roar of silence rhythming
Music from murmur; fragrance that enwreathes
The setting sky's roseate slumberings;
Mild dew whose dusk-bred wine, moist on the lips,
One moment's impulse blood inspires and streams
Vino Sacristi *that the soul's mouth sips;*
Soothe southern air; and gentle among dreams –
Drifting down sudden starlight's shafted fire –
Sensed intimations of unsensed desire.

Who is my Lord, my Shepherd is; I lack
For nothing. He who feeds me, leads me by
Life's waters. He who shields me, yields me back
To sheltered paths; safe in his care am I.
Although the night is dark, I faint nor fear
For he has lit a lantern to affright
My enemies. My trust he does revere
For he who blest me, drest me in his light.
I am content: he loves me, and will give
His love to me through all my days, and well
He promises that with him I shall live.
Forever in my Shepherd's love I dwell.

IAN SLATER was born in Cheshire in 1943 where for the most part of his life he lived in a small country village until circumstance placed him in various other parts of the world.

This book, compiled over several years, contains glimpses of the long-loved Arcadia for which the author yearns and which are drawn from memories of the past mingled with the experience of the present as viewed through the eyes of the exile during his numerous visits to scenes and influences of his youth and childhood.

At present Ian Slater is warden of Friends Meeting House in Great Yarmouth.